MW00635844

Inspired Work
Showing Up & Shining Bright

WORKBOOK

Erin Ramsey

Inspired Work: Showing Up & Shining Bright Workbook

No part of this publication may be reproduced in any form or by any means, including scanning, photocopying, or otherwise without prior written permission of the copyright holder or publisher except for brief passages in connection with a review.

Printed in the United States of America

General editing: Sierra Bower

Author photo by Krista Wedding, Grace James Photography

Cover design: Grace Winiger

Living Inspired, LLC

Copyright © 2017 Erin Ramsey

ISBN-10: 0998443840

ISBN-13: 978-0998443843

KNOWING IS NOT ENOUGH; WE MUST APPLY. WILLING IS NOT ENOUGH; WE MUST DO.

~

GOETHE

CONTENTS

TO THE BRAVE ONES.

Introduction

This workbook is based on the book, *Inspired Work: Showing Up & Shining Bright*. The truth is that having inspiration in your life takes concerted effort. We need to break old thought patterns, behaviors and responses that block our best selves from showing up and shining bright. The path to working with inspiration doesn't need to be painful or perfect. All you need to do is get on the path and start using some of the tools.

The intended use of this Workbook is for teams and leaders to go through the activities together with authentic communication and true effort to create space and cultures that provide opportunities for everyone to thrive. In the end, we are all responsible for our experiences. We can't blame work, the boss, the pay or anything outside of ourselves.

This Workbook can also be used alone in conjunction with *Inspired Work* for you to apply the tools to your entire life, both at work and at home.

It is my hope that you will give yourself the gift of growth because it is energizing. When we learn new things, try new things and celebrate everything we are doing well we have greater chances of working with inspiration.

The activities in this workbook will provide strategies that will guide you in practicing using the tools in *Inspired Work*, as well as, build relationships and action plans with your co workers grounded in purpose and trust.

Each tool has three components:

Ponder

This is the section where you really take some time to think about the tool and how it is relevant in your life. This is where you look in the mirror. Take time to think in new ways and consider where you are and where you want to go.

✓ Practice & Plan

This is the section where you add on to your reflection by doing something to use the tool. This is where the rubber hits the road. This is your chance to walk the talk. **If you are in a group study, this is where team members can report out their action steps and thoughts.**

Propel Yourself

This is the section where you set goals and plan action steps to making this tool accessible in your everyday life in order to take you to the next level of being amazing.

This is your workbook so take your time. Skip around. Focus on what you are willing and able to do so you set yourself up for success. Use colored pens, doodle, highlight and tab things. Have fun!

Inspiration Baseline

As you respond to the following statements think about the last month so you have a current view of where you are. Be honest with yourself. This tool is for you to determine where you want to put your energy going forward.

Circle where you are on each of these statements using this scale:

1=No/Never

4=Maybe/Sometimes

7=Yes/Always

I have a clear vision of my biggest dreams and greatest contributions. I know what I want for my life.

1 2 3 4 5 6 7

I am aware of how my thoughts influence what happens in my life and work.

1 2 3 4 5 6 7

I align my actions to how I want to be remembered.

1 2 3 4 5 6 7

I know what I stand for and I act with integrity.

1 2 3 4 5 6 7

I feel significant and know that I have impact on others in both negative and positive ways.

1   2   3   4   5   6   7

I know how to keep myself from getting depleted and I have many healthy activities that I enjoy.

1   2   3   4   5   6   7

I do many things well at work. I feel good about what I am contributing.

1   2   3   4   5   6   7

I carefully choose how I use my time because I know what my priorities are.

1   2   3   4   5   6   7

I know when I am ready for a new challenge.

1   2   3   4   5   6   7

I take action to challenge myself.

1   2   3   4   5   6   7

I am trustworthy, I don't gossip and I keep my word.

1   2   3   4   5   6   7

I have many people I trust.

1   2   3   4   5   6   7

I work well with others. I get along with most people.

1   2   3   4   5   6   7

I am comfortable with open and honest communication.

1   2   3   4   5   6   7

I accept others easily.

1   2   3   4   5   6   7

I listen to others. I really want to understand them.

1   2   3   4   5   6   7

I look for and see the good in most situations and people. I believe there is more good than bad.

1   2   3   4   5   6   7

I feel joyful and have a high energy level most of the time.

1   2   3   4   5   6   7

I see beautiful things and experience beautiful moments almost every day.

1   2   3   4   5   6   7

I choose my responses to people and situations and rarely overreact or get angry.

1   2   3   4   5   6   7

When faced with a challenge, I look for solutions instead of complaining.

1   2   3   4   5   6   7

I actively look for ways I can help others.

1   2   3   4   5   6   7

I am often times curious.

1   2   3   4   5   6   7

I come up with new ideas.

1   2   3   4   5   6   7

I am always learning new things.

1   2   3   4   5   6   7

Add all of the numbers in each response for your score.

Total Score: _____   Date: _____

Inspiration Baseline Score

175-125: You are inspired in many ways and open to all of your gifts, talents, and possibilities. Keep working to challenge yourself in areas you may have scored lower or in areas that you are most curious about. This is a good time in your life to create new challenges.

124-75: You are ready to find new ways to shine bright and increase your contributions. You are doing some things to be inspired but should be looking for areas that will increase your positive energy and generate new possibilities.

74-25: You are ready to start a new path to break out of unhealthy thought patterns and situations. You may be in a rut and looking for things to get you inspired. You are worthy and can do it!

Without judgment, think about where you are on the Inspiration Baseline. Now make a commitment to increase the baseline as you work through this book. Meet yourself where you are. Our lives go in cycles - this is an opportunity to create a positive cycle. You don't have to be perfect or inspired all of the time. The goal is to choose where you want to try new things, thought patterns and ways of working. All you have to do is make small changes and before you know it you will be creating a life of inspiration. Let's stop watching the clock and start living.

Inspired Work
Operating Premises

We are intended to live joyously and abundantly.

It isn't what we do but how we do it that matters.

We are not what happens to us; we are how we respond to what

happens.

We shouldn't use work as a scapegoat to our happiness.

We need each other.

When we shine bright we light the way for others.

There is more good than bad. What we focus on we get more of.

Focus on love not fear.

Our lives are a reflection of our choices.

It is never too late to make different choices.

Clarity of Purpose

Life is found in the dance between your deepest desire and your greatest fear.

~Tony Robbins

Everything to Gain

The secret of change is to focus all of your energy, not on fighting the old, but on building the new. ~Socrates

🗨 Ponder

What are a few things you would like to change about your current work situation? It could be anything, your hours, your relationships, your compensation or duties.

What are a few things you really love about your current work?

Everything to Gain

✓ *Practice & Plan*

Make time to think about what you really want at work. Use what you don't like and switch them into to what you want. Use what you do like and make them even better. Practice thinking boldly so you create space for the biggest dreams that are deep in your heart. You will discover dreams you don't even know I have. **Write down 5 statements in present tense of how you want work to be.**

Now make a few notes about what you can do differently to make these things happen.

Erin Ramsey

Everything to Gain

☀ *Propel Yourself*

How old will you be in 5 years? _____

When you are _____ how would your picture perfect life look and feel?

Draw a picture or write a description of your biggest boldest dreams for yourself in 5 years.

Affirmation

I am worthy of receiving abundance and living joyfully. My vision of my life and my work is big and bold. I dream big to help others do the same. My big vision and greatest contributions are my right and my responsibility. I have everything to gain.

Create New Thoughts Patterns

What you think you become. What you feel, you attract. What you imagine, you create. ~Buddha

🗨 Ponder

What are some common thoughts you have that may be holding you back from feeling good, from being optimistic, dreaming big and being inspired?

Create New Thoughts Patterns

✓ *Practice & Plan*

Pay careful attention to your thoughts. Create new thought patterns to expand the possibilities for your life.

Common negative thought:

New inspired thought:

Common negative thought:

New inspired thought:

Create New Thoughts Patterns

☀ *Propel Yourself*

I am thinking big, believing big and being bold because I know when I shine bright I light the way for others.

Make a list of big and bold thoughts of abundance in your work and your life, your dreams and feelings about yourself and others. Even if it feels weird or outlandish do it anyway. Practice saying them and thinking them.

Work Life Backwards

Strive not be a success but rather to be of value. ~Albert Einstein

🗩 Ponder

Think back on the last two weeks. Visualize what you did, who you interacted with, how you did your work, cared for your loved ones and treated yourself. Were you laughing and spreading joy? Were you present and engaged? Were you rushing and distracted? Exhausted and depleted? Healthy and vibrant? If you were to be remembered for the last two weeks, how would people remember you? Write down your thoughts.

Work Life Backwards

✓ *Practice & Plan*

Embrace yourself and all of the gifts you have to offer others. Shine bright. Write down your best life eulogy. What do you want people to say about you at your funeral?

Work Life Backwards

☀ Propel Yourself

Affirmation

I align my actions, thoughts and decisions with how I want to be remembered. I am in a proactive state working towards the life I dream of even when it is hard and stressful.

Write down what you are going to do differently to align with how you want to be remembered, at work and at home.

Make a Declaration

Your beliefs become your thoughts,

Your thoughts become your words,

Your words become your actions,

Your actions become your habits,

Your habits become your values; your values become your destiny.

~Mahatma Gandhi

Ponder

What do you believe in?

What do you value for yourself and others?

What are you willing to work for?

What is most important to you?

Tip: You can look up lists of values online to get yourself started.

Make a Declaration

✓ *Practice & Plan*

A Declaration is your manifesto, a document stating your values, beliefs and goals. Write down your Declaration. Here are few prompts that may help you get started: My life and work are grounded in, I believe in, I will stand up for, I will work towards, I trust, or The answer is...

✳ *Propel Yourself*

Affirmation
I take the time to know myself. I make the investment of time in myself - it is more important than taking time to buy a car or plan a vacation. The time I take to declare who I am has far greater returns for the quality of my life. I know clarity is the first step in living and working with inspiration.

Purpose

When you express your unique talents and use them in the service of humanity, you create abundance in your life and the lives of others. ~Deepak Chopra

How can you serve?

💭 *Ponder*

What did you love to do and play as a child?

What are some things that come naturally to you and are helpful to others?

What do people say you are good at?

Group Tip: If you are doing this in a group it is a good idea for everyone to share the gifts they see in each other.

Purpose

✓ *Practice & Plan*

Make time to think about and articulate your purpose through the lens of service. Write a few sentences that describe your special gifts and why you may have them. It may take awhile and effort to get clarity on your purpose. Don't give up. This activity is a good start.

Purpose

☀ Propel Yourself

Affirmation

I am clear on my purpose. I am brave and accountable for the gifts I have been granted.

Draw or write how you feel or will feel by having clarity of your purpose.

Thoughts & Notes

about Clarity of Purpose

AHAs

Feelings of Resistance

Bold Action

Heightened Self Awareness

You are built not to shrink down to less, but to blossom into more. To be more splendid. To be more extraordinary.

~Oprah Winfrey

Present of Presence

Plenty of people miss their share of happiness, not because they never found it, but because they didn't stop to enjoy it.

~William Feather

💭 Ponder

What are your biggest distractions? Phone, television, worry, rushing? Why are these things distracting you?

Present of Presence

✓ *Practice & Plan*

Look for beautiful moments. Write down and talk about good things. Make efforts to connect with others and limit your distractions. Write or draw a few recent beautiful moments. Make a plan to practice not using technology or your biggest distractors at work and at home.

Present of Presence

☀ Propel Yourself

Affirmation
I savor the present moment because I know that the moment is all we have. I embrace presence and grant myself the beautiful gift of being in the moment.

Write down how you are going to be more present at work.

Write down how you are going to be more present at home.

Be Your Own Coach

Between stimulus and response there is space. In that space is our power to

choose our response. In our response lies our growth and our freedom.

~Viktor E. Frankl

Ponder

Think about what triggers you to get reactive. Which people, times of the day or situations make you upset, grumpy, angry or frustrated? Why do these reactions happen?

Be Your Own Coach

✓ *Practice & Plan*

Practice becoming aware of when you have negative reactions and will create new ways of responding. Hone in on things that trigger you to be reactionary and start practicing new ways of responding. Record something that you changed a common response to below.

Normally I would be reactive to this:

I now respond like this to be proactive:

Normally I would be reactive to this:

I now respond like this to be proactive:

Normally I would be reactive to this:

I now respond like this to be proactive:

Be Your Own Coach

☀ Propel Yourself

Affirmation
I choose how I respond and react and I have the power to manage my moods and my thoughts. I know how I am feeling influences how I live my life. I choose where to put my focus.

Write or draw how you will feel, how you will be interacting and performing at work if you learn to stay in a proactive state of mind.

Do Things You Enjoy

Life is 10% what happens to you and 90% how you react to it.
~Charles R. Swindoll

◌ Ponder

What do you like to do or have that can be done during a 'normal' day in your life? List as many thing you can think of.

Do Things You Enjoy

✓ *Practice & Plan*

Do at least one thing a day that you enjoy. Make it a priority and stay positive through the choices you make. Write or draw what you did for seven days below. Share with others.

☀ **Propel Yourself**

Affirmation
I am intended to live joyously and abundantly. I choose to enjoy my life.

Best Foot Forward

Little things make big things happen.

~John Wooden

💭 Ponder

Think about the way you show up to work, both mentally and physically. If you were from another planet and you greeted you in the morning at work what would you think of you? Write down your answers.

Look around at your environment, your duties, your physical appearance and demeanor, your interactions and all of the details, is everything done well and with care, even the smallest of tasks? Is your work a reflection of your best self?

Best Foot Forward

✓ *Practice & Plan*

Pay attention to how you are showing up in the world. Take action to always put your best foot forward. Write down a few things you are going to pay careful attention to so your actions represent your best and highest self. Write down a few areas where you will try harder to put your best foot forward, at home and at work.

☀ **Propel Yourself**

Affirmation

I matter. My name means something.

Stop Numbing Your Greatness

From the beginning, the key to renewal has been casting off of old skin.

~Mark Nepo

Ponder

When you do underestimate your impact at work?

When do you feel how important you are?

Stop Numbing Your Greatness

✓ *Practice & Plan*

Actively look for ways to make things better at work and at home. Know you have impact and make your impact positive by sharing ideas, working with integrity and shining bright. Write down a few things you want to do better for yourself and those around you.

☀ **Propel Yourself**

Affirmation
I am free of guilt and self-doubt. I have healthy routines and habits that serve as platforms for me to serve others, work toward my vision and align with my priorities.

Burn Up What No Longer Serves You

Let go or be dragged. ~Zen Proverb

⌂ *Ponder*

What are some things you can stop doing or thinking that hold you back from being inspired at work and in life? Is it complaining, being the victim, guilt, worry, regret, judgment, negative thought patterns, self doubt, fear?

Burn Up What No Longer Serves You

✓ *Practice & Plan*

Make a list of what no longer serves you and that you are willing to let go of. Burn it or rip it up and say good bye to it. Be aware of the things inside yourself that you let get in the way of being inspired. Choose to focus on what you want and how you can serve. Release the things that don't serve you.
Write the things that no longer serve you.

☀ Propel Yourself

Life Affirmation
I embrace all that serves me because I know it will help me serve others.

Thoughts & Notes

about Heightened Self Awareness

AHAs

Feelings of Resistance

Bold Action

Affinity for Action

You are what you do, not what you say you'll do.

~Carl Jung

Be a Doer, Not a Talker

Don't put off until tomorrow what you can do today. ~Benjamin Franklin

Ponder

What types of things do you procrastinate?

What do you love to do and do well at work?

Be a Doer, Not a Talker

✓ *Practice & Plan*

Reflect on your behaviors at work regarding doing and talking. Interrupt procrastinating thoughts and behaviors with action. Look for opportunities to be a proactive doer. Write down a few things that you are going to do immediately so they don't drain your energy thinking about doing them.

✳ Propel Yourself

Affirmation

I am a doer. I act on my ideas. I actively look for ways to be a problem solver.

Develop some ideas on how you can be a doer. Write about people who you know that are great problem solvers. Write about all of your assets in this area.

Routines and Rituals

When you discipline yourself, you're essentially training yourself to act in a specific way. Stay with this long enough and it becomes routine-in other words habit. So when you see people who look like 'disciplined' people, what you're really seeing is people who've trained a handful of habits into their lives. ~Gary Keller

🗨 Ponder

Think about how your day unfolds. Do you set time aside to think, plan and reflect? Do you do things you enjoy and things that are healthy?

✓ Practice & Plan

Make a plan to create healthy rituals in the morning, midday and in the evening. Build on what you are already doing to care for yourself and move in the direction of what you really want, at work and at home.

Routines and Rituals

☀ Propel Yourself

Affirmation

I navigate my life and my time in an abundant, productive ways through rituals. My habits propel me toward the biggest vision for my life. I work well and live happily.

My Routines and Rituals

Morning

Midday

Evening

Progress not Perfection

Continuous effort-not strength or intelligence - is the key to unlocking our potential. ~Winston Churchill

Ponder

When was the last time you tried something new or learned something that was challenging?

What areas at work would you like to get better at?

Progress not Perfection

✓ Practice & Plan

Pick something you want to get good at and embrace the process of practicing and progression. Record what happened.

☀ Propel Yourself

Affirmation

I am always learning and growing. I enjoy the process of progression.

Run TO Not Away

Wherever you go there you are.

~Jon Kabat Zinn

💭 Ponder

What do you want more of in your life and at work?

What barriers exist? How can you put your focus more on what you want and less on what you don't want?

Run TO Not Away

✓ *Practice & Plan*

Think about what you want and take action in that direction. When you come to a decision ask yourself: I am running TO something or away from something with this choice? Write down an example.

☀ Propel Yourself

Affirmation

I am clear on what I want. My decisions are based on what I want, not what I don't want.

Be Solution Oriented

The most successful person makes a habit of doing what the failing person doesn't like to do. ~Thomas Edison

💭 Ponder

How do you behave when challenges arise at work?

Do you immediately start to think of solutions and options or do you wait for others to figure it out?

Write about a person you know who is a great solution finder.

Be Solution Oriented

✓ *Practice & Plan*

Pay attention to how you respond to challenges and uncomfortable feelings. Practice looking for solutions. Resist being stagnant and negative. Grow and explore your options in all situations. Record a few examples of when you did or will do this.

☀ Propel Yourself

Affirmation
I am capable and willing to be solution oriented in all matters. I have control over myself and my responses. I make the choice to be abundant and proactive in my thinking.

Thoughts & Notes

about Affinity for Action

AHAs

Feelings of Resistance

Bold Action

Erin Ramsey

Put People First

If only you could sense how important you are to the lives of those you meet; how important you can be to people you may never even dream of. There is something of yourself that you leave at every meeting with another person.

~Fred Rogers

Who is packing your parachute?

We could put our lives in each other's hands without a second thought.

~Mr. Riecken

💬 Ponder

What does trust look and feel like? Write down your thoughts or draw pictures of how it feels.

Who is packing your parachute?

✓ *Practice & Plan*

Look for ways to build trust with others. Focus on building relationships with the people at work and at home with trust as the priority. Be a person of trust. List a few ways you will build more trust at work.

Group Tip: Everyone can share how they define trust.

☀ **Propel Yourself**

Affirmation

I trust others and I am trustworthy.

Let People Be Who They Are

As we learn to have compassion for ourselves, the circle of compassion for other-what and whom we can work with, and how becomes wider. ~Pema Chodron

☺ Ponder

Do you accept yourself? Why or why not?

Do you accept other people, even if they do things differently or believe differently than you do?

Do you find yourself trying to make other people do what you want them to do?

Let People Be Who They Are

✓ *Practice & Plan*

Identify when you pass judgment or try to change someone else. Write down how you are going to let others be who they are. You can only change yourself.

☀ Propel Yourself

Affirmation
I accept myself. I easily accept others. I have many healthy relationships.

I've Got Your Back!

We rise when we lift others.
~Unknown

🗨 *Ponder*

Do people encourage you when you are doing hard things?

Do you encourage others when they are doing hard things?

✓ *Practice & Plan*

Look for ways to support and encourage others just as they are. Notice when people are doing hard things and tell them you have their back. Write down two times you encourage someone lately.

☀ **Propel Yourself**

Affirmation

I am the one that helps others soar. I am the one who has others' back. I actively share my encouragement.

Listen to Hear

When you talk, you are only repeating what you already know. But if you listen, you may learn something new. ~Dalai Lama

🗨 Ponder

Do you listen to hear others? Why or why not? Give examples.

Listen to Hear

✓ *Practice & Plan*

Intentionally practice listening to hear. identify times when you are distracted and compare the experience to times when you are not. Develop strategies to be present and truly listen by setting your own thoughts and views to the side.

Distracted experience:

Present experience:

Distracted experience:

Present experience:

☀ **Propel Yourself**

Affirmation

I connect with others. I have an open heart and an open mind. I help others feel understood and seen.

Courageous Communication

Be brave enough to start a conversation that matters. ~Dau Voire

💭 Ponder

How well do you communicate what you want?

How well do you talk about challenges?

How well do you communicate when you feel hurt or angry?

Courageous Communication

✓ *Practice & Plan*

Focus on being courageous in the ways you communicate especially when you feel hurt or apprehensive. Write down a time that you practiced courageous communication instead of cowardly communication.

Courageous Communication

☀ Propel Yourself

Affirmation
I am courageous. I can be vulnerable by being honest and open. My focus is on solutions.

Courageous Communication includes:

- Expressing our true feelings without blame
- Asking questions
- Focusing on solutions and understanding
- Keeping the other persons' feelings and views with respect
- Not attacking
- Listening to hear
- Not taking it personal
- Being accountable
- Sharing ideas
- Admitting when we don't have the answer

Cowardly Communication includes:

- Deflection of frustration and defensiveness onto the what the other person is doing and saying
- Withdrawing and being a victim
- Making excuses for not being open and honest
- Gossiping
- Complaining
- Always having to be right

Thoughts & Notes

about Putting People First

AHAs

Feelings of Resistance

Bold Action

Vibrant Energy

There are only two ways to live your life. One is as though nothing is a miracle.

The other is a though everything is a miracle.

~Albert Einstein

Take the High Road

Whoever is careless with the truth in small matters cannot be trusted with important matters. ~Albert Einstein

Ponder

Write about someone you work with who demonstrates integrity. Be descriptive about how they act and what they think.

✓ Practice & Plan

Intentionally reflect on all the ways you are interacting, talking, thinking, letting go, standing up for and willing to act on. Make sure your actions and thoughts are seamlessly connected to your values. Write down how your actions align with your values at work.

Take the High Road

☀ Propel Yourself

Affirmation

I take the high road under all circumstances. I am a person of integrity.

Integrity is:
- Admitting mistakes and being accountable.
- Asking for help instead of worrying about how you look.
- Saying you are sorry.
- Doing your work to the best of your ability all of the time; not just when it is easy or convenient.
- Being authentic with your words and your thoughts.
- Never cheating.
- If a piece of clothing falls off the rack you pick it up.
- If you have a gum wrapper you put it in your pocket; you never litter.
- Never lying.
- Not gossiping.
- Stopping conversations that don't lift up others.
- Avoiding drama.
- Never talking poorly about someone else to feel better or look better or for any reason.
- Never taking a short cut that you wouldn't take if someone was watching.
- Treating everyone fairly and with respect; especially those that can't offer you anything.
- Giving credit where credit is due, no matter what.
- Being transparent with your actions and motives.
- Not trying to get something for free or ask for advantages if you don't really need them.

Be Hard to Offend

To offer no resistance to life is to be in a state of grace, ease and lightness.

~Eckhart Tolle

💭 Ponder

When was the last time you felt offended? Why?

✓ Practice & Plan

Notice when you are feeling offended. Step back and look at the whole situation. Ask yourself if you are taking it personally. Set boundaries; be responsive, not reactive. Use courageous communication. Write about a time how you went from offended to courageous.

☀ Propel Yourself

Affirmation

I am hard to offend. I live with my life grace and ease.

Expect the Best & Give the Benefit of the Doubt

It is better to light a candle than to curse the darkness.

~Chinese Proverb

Ponder

Do you expect the best when trying something new or when asked to enter a new situation?

Do you give others the benefit of the doubt when mistakes are made?

What does the 'benefit of the doubt' mean to you?

Think of a time when someone gave you the benefit of the doubt. How did it feel?

Expect the Best & Give the Benefit of the Doubt

✓ *Practice & Plan*

Look for opportunities to expand your thinking to include the benefit of the doubt and expecting the best more often than not. Treat each new encounter and new situation as a clean slate to open your mind and your heart.

Write about what you did recently to give the benefit of the doubt to someone at work.

Write about a recent time you expected the best even when you weren't certain of the situation at work.

☀ **Propel Yourself**

Affirmation

I am open minded and open hearted. I am mindful and optimistic.

What will bring the most joy?

True joy results when we become aware of our connectedness to everything.

~Paul Pearsail

🗨 *Ponder*

How do you decide what to commit to? What do you use as your guide in making decisions?

What type of attitude do you approach your work with?

On a scale of 1 to 10, 10 being all of the time, how joyful are you at work?

What will bring the most joy?

✓ *Practice & Plan*

Assess your conversations, your routines and rituals, and your thought patterns for maximizing joy.

What can you do to create more joy for yourself and those around you? Make a list.

☀ **Propel Yourself**

Affirmation

I am joyful in all that I do and I think.

Be a Giver, Not a Taker

The heart that gives, gathers.

~Tao Te Ching

💭 Ponder

If your coworkers were asked if you were a giver or a taker what would they answer?
Why?

✓ Practice & Plan

Enter situations with a giving attitude and giving action.
What can you do and what have you done to be a more of a giver than taker
at work? How are you approaching things from a lens of service, rather than
trying to figure out what you can get? Write 4 things you are going to do to
increase a giving attitude to those you work with, including the leaders.

☀ Propel Yourself

Affirmation
I am a giver.

Thoughts & Notes

about Vibrant Energy

AHAs

Feelings of Resistance

Bold Action

Make Room for Possibilities

Great minds discuss ideas.

Average minds discuss events.

Small minds discuss people.

~Eleanor Roosevelt

Follow the Nudge

The intuitive mind is a sacred gift and the rational mind is a faithful servant. We have created a society that honors the servant and has forgotten the gift.

~Albert Einstein

💭 Ponder

Do you follow your intuition?

✓ Practice & Plan

Slow down to listen and act on new ideas, feelings and situations. Consider trusting your intuition in small things through practice. Write down a few things you have noticed.

☀ Propel Yourself

Affirmation

My intuition is my guide.

Be Curious

When you are curious you find lots of interesting things to do.

~Walt Disney

🗨 *Ponder*

What was the last ting you were curious about and took action to learn more about at work and at home?

Be Curious

✓ *Practice & Plan*

Create space to be curious. Take action and pursue what you are curious about. Draw or write about any new thoughts, ideas or interests that you have created space for.

☀ **Propel Yourself**

Affirmation
My curiosity leads me to my greatness.

Let's Experiment

Doubt will kill more dreams than failure ever will. ~Suzy Kassen

💭 Ponder

When was the last time you felt free to explore something new, try something you were afraid to do or accepted 'failure' as a learning opportunity? Write your experience and your feelings about it.

✓ Practice & Plan

Next time you get a thought, a feeling, or an idea experiment with it. Follow the nudge and act on it. Replace fear with experiments. Write or draw what happened.

☀ Propel Yourself

Affirmation

I am free to explore all that life has to offer.

Pursue Your Passion

The things you are passionate about are not random. They are your calling.
~Fabienne Fredrickson

⬮ Ponder

What would you do if you weren't afraid?

What would you do if you won millions in the lottery?

Who do you admire and wish your life was more like theirs?

What are things you do that make time fly by?

What gets you fired up and angry?

What gets you excited and ready to take action?

Pursue Your Passion

✓ *Practice & Plan*

Intentionally look for ways to get in touch with your passion. Hold yourself accountable to your higher purposes. Write down what you noticed and discovered. Draw a picture of yourself pursuing a passion.

☀ **Propel Yourself**

Affirmation

My life is a reflection of what I care most about and my greatest contributions.

Keep Learning and Growing

You weren't born to just pay bills and die. ~Unknown

○ Ponder

What are some things you would like to learn more about in your job?

What are some things you would like to learn more about at home and in your life outside of work?

Keep Learning and Growing

✓ *Practice & Plan*

Notice when you are stagnant in your thinking and in your actions. Find things to learn about. Write or draw what you plan to or did learn more about. Include how you felt.

☀ **Propel Yourself**

Affirmation

I am always growing and learning.

Thoughts & Notes

about Making Room for Possibilities

AHAs

Feelings of Resistance

Bold Action

Conclusion

From My Heart to Yours

Dear Friend,

Today is your day. It is your time to show up and shine bright.

You are more than enough.

You are destined for greatness.

You are worthy of all that your heart desires.

Your beauty, your energy, and your heart will never fail you.

You already have everything you need.

Remember always:

> *You are intended to live joyously and abundantly.*
>
> *It isn't what you do but how you do it that matters.*
>
> *You are not what happens to you; you are how you respond to what happens.*
>
> *Don't use work as a scapegoat to your happiness.*
>
> *We need each other.*
> *When you shine bright you light the way for others.*
>
> *There is more good than bad. What you focus on you will get more of. Focus on love not fear.*
>
> *Your life is a reflection of your choices.*
>
> *It is never too late to make different choices.*

The moment is now.

With Love, Erin

ABOUT THE AUTHOR

Erin is an internationally sought after inspirational author and speaker. Erin has worked in the public sector for over twenty-five years in various leadership positions. She knows how to take ideas and put them into action and create teams that are inspiring and unique. She has a degree in child development and psychology as well as a master degree in public service administration.

She is the author of *Be Amazing: Tools for Living Inspired*, the *Be Amazing Workbook and Inspired Work: Showing Up & Shining Bright*. She has started a national movement to bring women together to share their dreams, fears and to learn together as they grow together. The platform is the POW WOWs, the power of women working on wonderful.

Erin resides in Kentucky where she and her family converted a cattle farm into a lavender farm. Their farm is called Big Roots and its purpose is to GROW PEACE. Big Roots is a place of rejuvenation and inspiration where day retreats with Erin are held. Visitors can cut their own lavender and flowers, walk the labyrinth and take in the beautiful countryside. Big Roots represents Erin's quest for living and working inspired!

To book Erin as a speaker for your event or to visit Big Roots you can email:

erin@erinramsey.com

To learn more about Erin's products and services you can visit: www.erinramsey.com

Erin's Family at Big Roots Farm

Grace, Luke, Sam, Ryan, Anna, Molly, Isabelle, Erin, Doug, Jack

Photo by Krista Wedding, Grace James Photography

Made in the USA
Columbia, SC
02 March 2023

13170579R00057